Dear Nan
from you to me®

JOURNALS®
of a LIFETIME
made with love *from you to me*

WWW.FROMYOUTOME.COM

Dear Nan

from you to me®

Dear Nan,

Here is a gift from me to you . . . for you to give to me.

When we are children we are always asking questions
. . . well I now have some more for you.

Please could you answer them in the way that only you know
how and then give the book back to me.

There might be a couple of questions that you prefer not to
answer, so don't worry, just answer the others as well as you
can . . . I won't mind.

People say that we all have at least one book in us, and this
will be one of yours.

The story of you and me that I will treasure forever.

Thank you,

with love

Tell me about the time and place you were born . . .

What are your earliest memories?

I'd like to know about your parents . . . names, dates of birth and tell me some stories about them . . .

Tell me what you know about your Mother's parents and family . . .

Tell me what you know about your Father's
parents and family . . .

Please detail what you know of our family tree . . .

What interesting information do you know about other people in our family?

Here's some space for you to add more about our family that will interest generations to come . . .

What do you remember about the place/s you lived when you were a child?

What were your favourite childhood toys or games?

What sort of pets did you have when you were young and what were their names?

What do you remember about your holidays as a child?

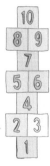

What did you do for entertainment when you were young?

What did you study at school and what were you best at?

Tell me about the things you did as a child that are different for today's children . . .

What did you want to do when you grew up?

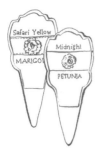

What were your favourite hobbies when you were young?

Did you have an idol when you were young?
Tell me who and why . . .

What was the first piece of music you bought?

What chores had to be done when you were young that aren't needed to be done today?

Describe any family traditions you had
or maybe still have . . .

What age were you when you started work?
Tell me about the jobs you have had . . .

How did you meet my Grandfather?

What would you do for a night-out when you were dating?

Tell me about a memorable piece of music that you and my Grandfather had 'just for you' . . .

Describe a special day you had with my
Grandfather . . .

Choosing the names for your children can be really difficult . . . how did you decide?

I would love to know more about my parents
. . . what can you tell me?

Tell me what my Mum / Dad was like
when they were younger . . .

How did you feel when you were told you were going to be a grandparent?

What did you think when you first saw me after I was born?

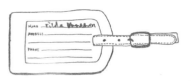

Can you see any characteristics in me that come from other people in our family?

In what ways am I similar or different to my Mum / Dad?

Describe some of your favourite memories of the times we have spent together . . .

Describe what you like about me . . .

Is there anything you would like to change

about me?

Tell me about the friends you have had in your life . . .

Yellow
Submarine

What piece/s of music would you choose in your own favourite 'top 10'?

Tell me about the most interesting places you have travelled to . . .

What are the happiest or greatest memories of your life?

What are a few of your favourite things?

Describe your memory of some major world events that have happened in your lifetime . . .

Describe the greatest change that you have seen in your lifetime so far . . .

Do you think life today is better or worse than when you were young? How is it different?

Who or what has been the greatest influence
on you?

If you were an animal . . . what type of animal would you be, and why?

If you won the Lottery . . . what would you do with the money?

What have you found most difficult in your life?

What is your **biggest regret** in your life?

Can you do anything about it **now**?

Tell me about the things that have made you happy or laugh . . .

With hindsight what would you do differently?

Describe something you still want to achieve in your life . . .

Tell me something you think I won't know about you . . .

How do you like to be thought of by others?

Given your experiences, what advice would you like to offer me?

And now your chance to tell me some other personal stories that you want to share . . .

These extra pages are for us to write any
questions, memories or answers that
may not have been covered elsewhere in the book . . .

And finally for the record . . .

what is your full name ?

what is your maiden name ?

what is your date of birth ?

what colour are your eyes ?

how tall are you ?

what blood group are you ?

what was the date when you completed this story for me ?

And a few words to thank you for completing this Journal of a Lifetime ...

Published by **FROM YOU TO ME**

For a full range of all our titles where journals
& books can also be personalised, please visit

WWW.FROMYOUTOME.COM

Dear Nan

from you to me®

Sketch collection first published by JOURNALS OF A LIFETIME, an imprint of **FROM YOU TO ME LTD**, in January 2012. Dear Nan September 2021

1 3 5 7 9 11 13 15 14 12 10 8 6 4 2

ISBN 978-1-907860-58-4

Designed and published in the UK.

Printed and bound in China by Imago. This paper is manufactured from pulp sourced from forests that are legally and sustainably managed.

FROM YOU TO ME
Waterhouse
Waterhouse Lane
Monkton Combe
Bath, BA2 7JA, UK

HELLO@FROMYOUTOME.COM

WWW.FROMYOUTOME.COM

JOURNALS®
of a LIFETIME

made with love *from you to me*